Graphic Organizers for Social Studies Classes

by Daniel J. Barnekow

illustrated by Marcellus Hall

J. WESTON
WALCH
PUBLISHER

Portland, Maine

User's Guide
to
Walch Reproducible Books

As part of our general effort to provide educational materials that are as practical and economical as possible, we have designated this publication a "reproducible book." The designation means that purchase of the book includes purchase of the right to limited reproduction of all pages on which this symbol appears:

Here is the basic Walch policy: We grant to individual purchasers of this book the right to make sufficient copies of reproducible pages for use by all students of a single teacher. This permission is limited to a single teacher, and does not apply to entire schools or school systems, so institutions purchasing the book should pass the permission on to a single teacher. Copying of the book or its parts for resale is prohibited.

Any questions regarding this policy or requests to purchase further reproduction rights should be addressed to:

Permissions Editor
J. Weston Walch, Publisher
321 Valley Street · P.O. Box 658
Portland, Maine 04104-0658

1   2   3   4   5   6   7   8   9   10

ISBN 0-8251-3768-3

Contents

Preface

This book was conceived of as a kind of "Swiss Army knife" for social studies teachers. The idea was to create a teaching resource that would be there when you needed it, help you accomplish a wide variety of tasks, and get you out of some tough teaching spots.

That was the idea. The result is this book. Between its covers, you'll find a quick, prepared, practical assignment for virtually every major topic you're likely to cover in your social studies classes. What's more, each assignment is designed to teach, reinforce, and extend the key concepts of the social studies curriculum. This was accomplished by combining a teaching technique that has proven pedagogical value with national social studies curriculum standards.

You can draw on the student activity sheets in *Graphic Organizers for Social Studies Classes* nearly any school day. At your fingertips you'll have a ready-made, easy-to-use, pedagogically valuable lesson on nearly any topic. The lessons will be popular with students, and are suitable for either in-class or homework assignments.

We wish you, and your students, the best of luck in your endeavors.

My appreciation is extended to Lisa French, for her support while I assembled this book. More thanks go to the social studies teachers and, especially, their students, without whose insights this book would not be possible.

—*Daniel J. Barnekow*

To the Teacher

A teacher once described graphic organizers as "sophisticated doodles." In a way, he was right. In fact, that may be the best way for you to think about graphic organizers and to present them to your students. You can find many jargon-laden articles and books that analyze graphic organizers, put forth new taxonomies, and labor to link them to psychological dynamics. These have their place, of course, but graphic organizers—essentially a simple teaching tool—have been over-analyzed, with the net effect of confusing rather than enlightening educators.

Graphic Organizers for Social Studies Classes is designed to cut through the jargon and give you a practical tool that you can use immediately. By spending a little time reading this introduction and thumbing through the graphic organizers, you'll soon be ready to go.

Understanding Graphic Organizers

On a practical, classroom level, all you need to know about graphic organizers can be summed up in a few key points. As you use this book—or use graphic organizers in any educational context—keep these ideas in mind:

Graphic organizers are simply ways to organize information visually. This is a simple, straightforward, and accurate description of graphic organizers.

Graphic organizers are nearly always appropriate. Most people tend to think in visual terms, so graphic organizers are often an appropriate way to organize information on a page.

Graphic organizers come in many forms. Many attempts have been made to categorize graphic organizers and to identify them by type. You've probably heard of sequence chains, concept maps, webs, flow charts, Venn diagrams, and so on. (You'll find all of these in this book.) Some of the best graphic organizers are combinations of these standard forms, and some are utterly unique.

Graphic organizers are never right or wrong, only better or worse. Assuming that the information presented and its interrelationships are correct, there are no "wrong" graphic organizers. However, some do a better job of presenting the same information than others.

Graphic organizers are not communicative, but conceptual. They are tools that help students acquire knowledge, not a means of imparting knowledge. Obviously, graphic organizers are excellent communication tools, but in the classroom, you should focus on using them as a way for students to learn, not as a way to express what they've learned to you.

Graphic organizers are concept-driven. The form of the graphic organizer should follow its function, not vice versa.

Content and Organization: Major Fields, Key Concepts, and Main Ideas

This book covers a wide range of social studies topics, as a quick glance at the table of contents will show. The major sections of the book correspond to *major fields* taught in social studies classes. Within each major field, the graphic organizers emphasize *key concepts,* and each graphic organizer focuses on the *main ideas* of each key concept.

This organization enables you to use these graphic organizers throughout the year to help students achieve the principal learning objectives of your social studies classes.

Correlation to National Standards

The content and organization of *Graphic Organizers for Social Studies Classes* were inspired and guided by a respected set of national standards created under the direction of the National Council for the Social Studies (NCSS). The major sections of the book correspond to the ten major themes or strands presented in these standards. Each graphic organizer in this book supports one or more specific NCSS standards.

How to Use the Graphic Organizers in this Book

Of course, you can use these graphic organizers any way you see fit—they are flexible tools. You can use them for basal instruction, review, and extension and enrichment. You can have students work in pairs or small groups to complete them. They function equally well for homework and in-class assignments and are excellent guides for classroom discussion.

A Lesson Cycle for Individual Graphic Organizers: Educators have learned that following a few simple steps will help their students get the most out of their graphic organizers. These steps, tailored to the content of this book, are presented below in, well, a graphic organizer!

```
┌──────────────────────────────────────────────────────────────┐
│ 1. Familiarize yourself with the graphic organizer and the    │
│    teaching notes for it.                                      │
└──────────────────────────────────────────────────────────────┘
                              ↓
┌──────────────────────────────────────────────────────────────┐
│ 2. Explain or review what graphic organizers are and why      │
│    they're worthwhile. Emphasize the importance of organizing │
│    information.                                                │
└──────────────────────────────────────────────────────────────┘
                              ↓
┌──────────────────────────────────────────────────────────────┐
│ 3. Present the specific graphic organizer. Point out its      │
│    subject, its organizational framework, and the             │
│    introduction, direction line, and questions.               │
└──────────────────────────────────────────────────────────────┘
                              ↓
┌──────────────────────────────────────────────────────────────┐
│ 4. Model using the graphic organizer. Use examples. Consider  │
│    giving students an example of what to include in each      │
│    cell. If the graphic organizer calls for them to choose    │
│    its topic, provide them with options.                      │
└──────────────────────────────────────────────────────────────┘
                              ↓
┌──────────────────────────────────────────────────────────────┐
│ 5. Assign the graphic organizer as an individual, paired, or  │
│    group activity.                                            │
└──────────────────────────────────────────────────────────────┘
                              ↓
┌──────────────────────────────────────────────────────────────┐
│ 6. Review students' work. Use the Key Questions in the        │
│    Teaching Notes to generate classroom discussion or extend  │
│    individual student learning.                               │
└──────────────────────────────────────────────────────────────┘
```

How to Use the Graphic Organizers as a Set

Because *Graphic Organizers for Social Studies Classes* has nearly comprehensive topic coverage, inspired by national standards, you can use the organizers as curricular signposts, correlating them to the main points in your curriculum.

Also, because the graphic organizers emphasize *main ideas* in the *key concepts* of *major fields* in social studies, they are excellent material for student portfolios.

Teaching Notes

Teaching notes for each of the graphic organizers in this book are provided at the beginning of each major section in the text. The notes are organized in the following format:

[number]
[Title of Graphic Organizer]

Objective: *Identifies the major learning objective of the graphic organizer.*

Key Questions: *Key questions that generate classroom discussion, guide students in achieving the learning objective, and extend teaching about the subject of the graphic organizer*

Usage Notes: *Tips and techniques for using the graphic organizer most effectively and suggested answers where appropriate*

1.   Culture (anthropology)

I. Culture (anthropology)

C-1: What Is Culture?

Objective: Students will define culture and identify its significant characteristics.

Key Questions:

- What is culture?

- What are some examples of cultures?

- What things are part of every culture?

- What characteristics define a culture?

Usage Notes: You might need to guide students through the two blank cells under "Characteristics of every culture."

C-2: Understanding Cultural Diversity

Objective: Students will explain and explore cultural diversity.

Key Questions:

- What is cultural diversity?

- Why is it important?

- What are some examples of cultural diversity that you have encountered?

- How do human cultures form a sort of patchwork quilt?

- Why is cultural diversity beneficial?

Usage Notes: Emphasize the benefits of cultural diversity.

C-3: An Ethnography

Objective: Students will create an ethnographic profile of a culture.

Key Questions:

- What is an ethnography?

- Why are ethnographies useful?

- How can the characteristics be identified for each culture?

- How do ethnographies help you compare and contrast cultures?

Usage Notes: Assign this graphic organizer in conjunction with learning about particular cultures, countries, or regions. Distribute multiple copies to facilitate comparisons among different cultures.

C-4: Diversity in Your Community

Objective: Students will explore cultural diversity in their own community.

Key Questions:

- Questions formed from chart headings

- How does our community benefit from this diversity?

- How do you personally benefit from this diversity?

Usage Notes: Ensure that students are respectful when conducting research and discussing this topic.

Name _____ Date _____

C-1: What Is Culture?

Introduction: You've probably heard the word **culture** before. What do you think it means? In fact, culture can mean different things—and many things all at once. In fact, one researcher has located more than 300 different definitions for culture! Still, you are perfectly able to understand what culture means. After all, you belong to one. Your culture, along with the cultures of others, will play a fundamental role in your life. So it pays to have a good understanding of what the term really means. This activity will help with that.

• **Directions:** Complete the graphic organizer.

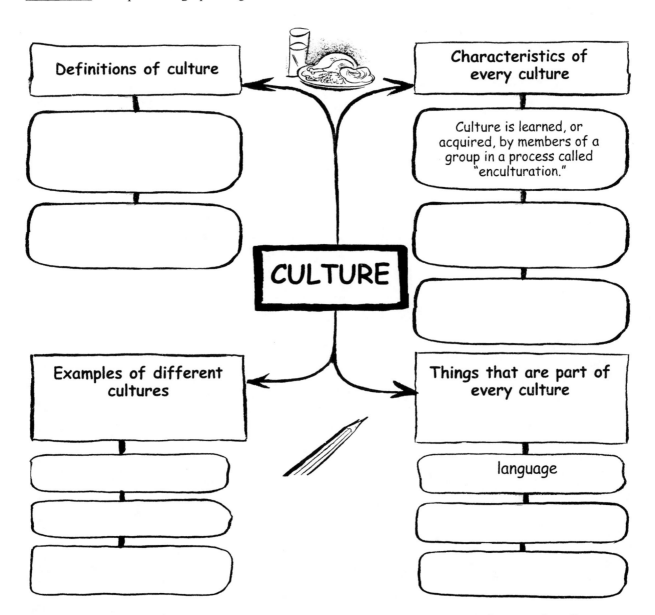

Definitions of culture

Characteristics of every culture

Culture is learned, or acquired, by members of a group in a process called "enculturation."

CULTURE

Examples of different cultures

Things that are part of every culture

language

Taking Another Step: Study the items you listed that are "Things that are part of every culture." On the back of this sheet, list the specific form that each item takes in your culture.

Name _____ Date _____

C-2: Understanding Cultural Diversity

Introduction: If you know that the word *diversity* means "variety," you're halfway to understanding what "cultural diversity" means. It's a phrase you need to understand. One of the great developments of the last 100 years is growing recognition and appreciation of the great cultural diversity of our country, and our world.

• **Directions:** Cultural diversity is often compared to a patchwork quilt. Each part is unique, but taken together, they form a whole. The "quilt" below represents this idea. Finish it by writing what you think under each patch's title.

Taking Another Step: On the back of this sheet, explain how cultural diversity is found at the local, national, and global levels.

Name _____ Date _____

C-3: An Ethnography

Introduction: An **ethnography** is a written description of a culture. Anthropologists and other people use ethnographies to learn about and compare cultures. You can create a chart to show the major characteristics that define a culture.

• **Directions:** Choose a cultural group to learn more about. Write its name on the line provided. Then, conduct research to complete the table.

An Ethnographic Profile of:	
_____ *(name of cultural group)*	
Characteristic	**Description**
location	
population	
history	
language	
religion	
economy	
food	
clothing	
shelter	
family life	
other: _____ _____	
other: _____ _____	

Taking Another Step: Use the notes you took in the chart to create a written ethnography on the back of this sheet.

Name _____ Date _____

C-4: Diversity in Your Community

Introduction: People from every corner of the globe have come to the United States, making it perhaps the most diverse country on earth. People from nearly every culture, who speak nearly every language in the world, live or have lived here. There are at least 120 distinct ethnic groups in the United States. Americans practice an amazing variety of religions. We are the product of the greatest immigration in history. How is this diversity reflected in your own community? To find out, follow the directions.

• **Directions:** Conduct research to complete the chart below.

Diversity in My Community	
Ethnic groups who live here	
Races of the people who live here	
Languages spoken here	
Religions practiced here	

Taking Another Step: Write a paragraph on the back of this sheet that explains how you found out the information included in your chart.

         Graphic Organizers for Social Studies Classes

II.   Time, Continuity, and Change (history)

TCC-1: Comparing and Contrasting Then and Now

Objective: Students will compare and contrast important features of a historical period with contemporary times.

Key Questions:

- How is each characteristic different?
- How is each characteristic the same?
- What characteristic did you add to the graphic organizer?

Usage Notes: You can use this graphic organizer in conjunction with studying any historical period. Students can also compare and contrast two historical periods by replacing "now" on the diagram with a historical period.

TCC-2: Major Periods in American History

Objective: Students will identify major periods in American history, date them, and identify major events, persons, and other characteristics associated with each.

Key Questions:

- What are the periods?
- Why is each one so-called?
- When did each one occur?
- What are the major events, persons, inventions, etc., associated with each period?
- How can you memorize these periods?

Usage Notes: This graphic organizer is designed for use with such common terms as the Colonial Period, the Revolutionary Period, the Era of Good Feelings, etc. Consider assigning it in conjunction with graphic organizer TCC-4.

TCC-3: Major Events in American History

Objective: Students will identify major events in American history, date them, and describe their significance.

Key Questions:

- What events did you include?
- When did each one happen?
- What is the significance of each?

Usage Notes: This graphic organizer can be used either for an overview of the whole of American history or to focus on events of a certain period. Consider assigning it in conjunction with graphic organizer TCC-5.

TCC-4: Answering Questions About a Historical Period

Objective: Students will answer six basic questions about a historical period.

Key Questions:

- Questions from the graphic organizer

Usage Notes: This graphic organizer is designed for use with any historical period. Encourage concise but complete answers. Consider assigning it in conjunction with graphic organizer TCC-2.

TCC-5: Answering Questions About a Historical Event

Objective: Students will answer six basic questions about a historical event.

Key Questions:

- Questions from the graphic organizer

Usage Notes: This graphic organizer is designed for use with any historical event. Encourage concise but complete answers. Consider assigning it in conjunction with graphic organizer TCC-3.

Name _____ Date _____

TCC-1: Comparing and Contrasting Then and Now

Introduction: Have you ever dreamed of traveling in a time machine? Well, you *can* do a sort of time traveling in your mind. Combine research with your own imagination to create a picture of life long ago.

• **Directions:** Complete the graphic organizer. For each topic, list practices, customs, tools and technologies, or other things that no longer prevail in the left-hand column. In the right-hand column, list things that prevail today but did not exist then. Write things that are part of both then and now in the center column.

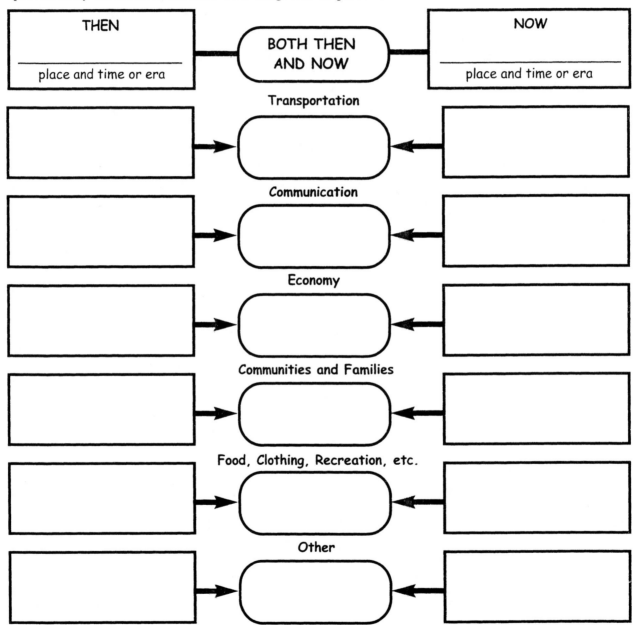

THEN _____ place and time or era

BOTH THEN AND NOW

NOW _____ place and time or era

Transportation

Communication

Economy

Communities and Families

Food, Clothing, Recreation, etc.

Other

Taking Another Step: Would you like to visit the time and place you described in the left-hand column? Why? Give your answer in the form of a paragraph on the back of this sheet.

               Graphic Organizers for Social Studies Classes

Name _____ Date _____

TCC-2: Major Periods in American History

Introduction: History is crowded with so many people and events that it can be difficult to keep track of them all. Even professional historians sometimes get confused. You can do what they do to help make sense of history: organize it in large segments of time, called **historical periods**. When you've learned these periods, it's easy to fit new information into them. It's like filling in an outline, or putting information into different file folders.

• **Directions:** Completing the diagram on the next page will help you learn and remember the major periods in American history. Use the Information to Include box as a guide.

Taking Another Step: A good way to help you memorize both the names and the order of the periods is to make up a silly sentence in which each word begins with the same letter as the names of the period. Make up such a sentence and write it on the back of this sheet.

(continued)

Name _____ Date _____

TCC-2: Major Periods in American History *(continued)*

Major Periods in American History

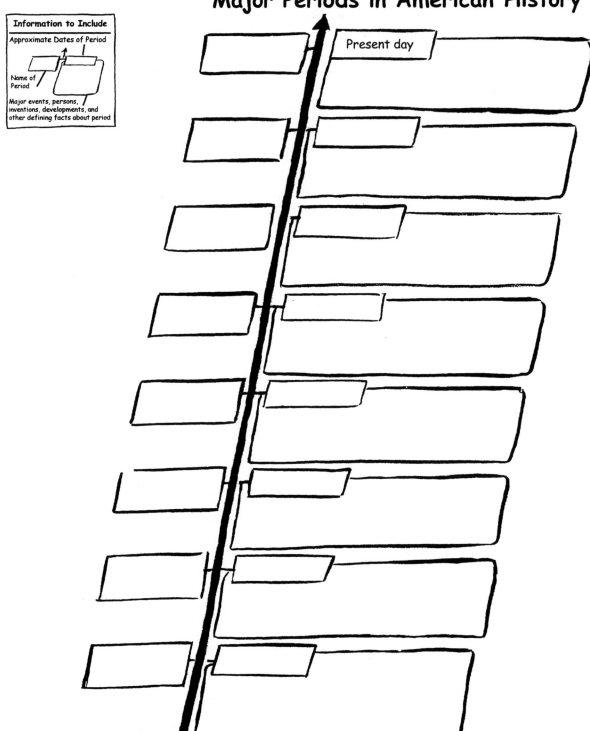

Information to Include

Approximate Dates of Period

Name of Period

Major events, persons, inventions, developments, and other defining facts about period

Present day

Name _____ Date _____

TCC-3: Major Events in American History

Introduction: You can learn about and remember important events in American history by arranging them in a kind of time line.

• **Directions:** Write the name and dates of the historical period on the line provided. Then, fill in each box with an important event that took place during the period.

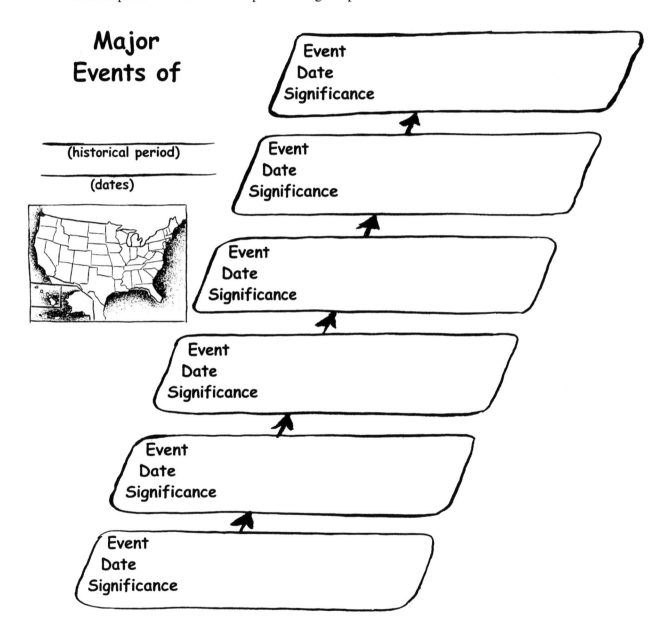

Major
Events of

_____
(historical period)
_____
(dates)

Event
Date
Significance

Event
Date
Significance

Event
Date
Significance

Event
Date
Significance

Event
Date
Significance

Event
Date
Significance

Taking Another Step: Choose the most important or interesting event that you included. Illustrate it in the space to the right of the time line. Draw an arrow from the box to the illustration to show which event you illustrated.

Name _____ Date _____

TCC-4: Answering Questions About a Historical Period

• **Directions:** Conduct research to complete the chart. Write short notes that answer the question in each box.

WHEN did this period occur?

WHAT important developments or events mark this period?

WHERE did the major events or developments of this period occur?

HISTORICAL PERIOD:

WHO are the important historical figures associated with this period?

WHY is this period important?

HOW did the events or developments of this period affect later periods in American history?

Taking Another Step: Expand one of your answer boxes into a paragraph. Write your paragraph on the back of this sheet.

Name _____ Date _____

TCC-5: Answering Questions About a Historical Event

• **Directions:** Conduct research to complete the chart. Write short notes that answer the question in each box.

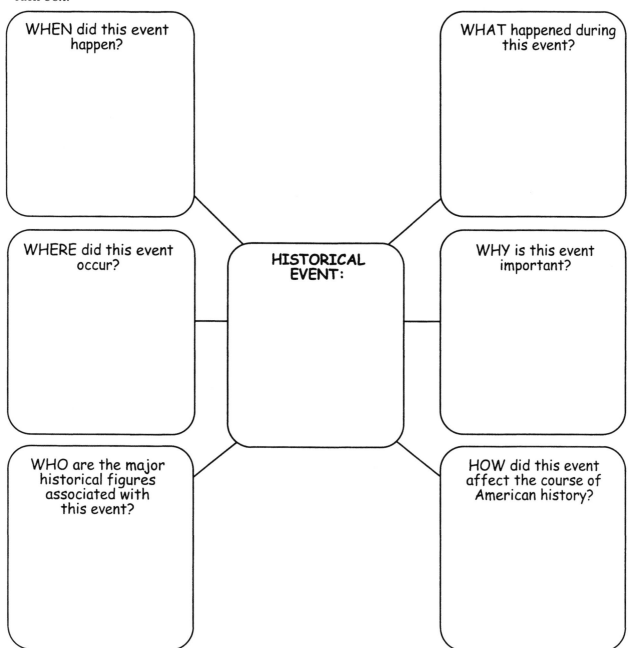

WHEN did this event happen?

WHAT happened during this event?

WHERE did this event occur?

HISTORICAL EVENT:

WHY is this event important?

WHO are the major historical figures associated with this event?

HOW did this event affect the course of American history?

Taking Another Step: Expand one of your answer boxes into a paragraph. Write your paragraph on the back of this sheet.

III.   People, Places, and Environments
(geography)

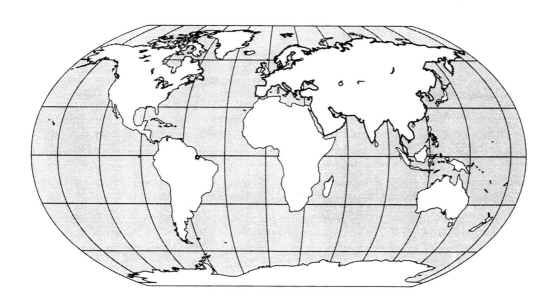

PPE-1: How to Read a Map

Objective: Students will explain the seven basic steps of map reading.

Key Questions:

- What are the seven basic steps in reading a map?

- Why is each one important?

- How might you take each step more than once when you use a map?

- How might you take these steps in different order?

Usage Notes: Consider assigning a particular map for students to use in conjunction with this graphic organizer. Encourage students to memorize the seven steps.

PPE-2: Locating a Place

Objective: Students will explore and apply techniques of absolute and relative location.

Key Questions:

- Questions formed from headings in the graphic organizer

- What does absolute location mean? Relative location? How are both useful?

- Why is the diagram shaped like an upside-down triangle?

Usage Notes: This graphic organizer can be used to locate any type of place. Assign it several times to give students practice.

PPE-3: Characteristics of a Place or a Region

Objective: Students will identify and describe the major characteristics of a place or a region.

Key Questions:

- Questions formed from headings in the graphic organizer

- What makes this place or region unique?

- How is it alike and different from other places?

- Why did you put each characteristic in the category that you did?

Usage Notes: Guide students in understanding and differentiating among the different groups of characteristics.

PPE-4: Profiling a Natural Feature

Objective: Students will create a profile of a natural feature.

Key Questions:

• Questions formed from headings in the graphic organizer

Usage Notes: You can either assign specific natural features for students to investigate or let them choose their own.

PPE-5: The Three Rs

Objective: Students will explain and give examples of the "three Rs" for reducing environmental pollution: reduce, reuse, and recycle.

Key Questions:

• What does reducing mean?

• What does reusing mean?

• What does recycling mean?

• What are some examples of each?

• How can you put each one into practice at home and at school?

Usage Notes: Encourage students to learn specific ways that they can implement each of the "three Rs," and reward them for putting them into practice.

Name _____ Date _____

PPE-1: How to Read a Map

Introduction: Every map of the world shows seven continents. This is a convenient way to remember that there are **seven steps to reading every map!**

• **Directions:** Each continent shown on the next page explains one step to reading a map. Read each step in order. Then answer each question on the back of this sheet.

Taking Another Step: When you use a map, you often jump back and forth between various steps. For example, you'll probably need to refer to both the scale and the key when you use a map to answer and ask questions. But, when you look at a map for the first time, you should try to do it systematically. Do *you* prefer to follow a different order than the one indicated above? If so, renumber the steps accordingly.

(continued)

Name _____ Date _____

PPE-1: How to Read a Map *(continued)*

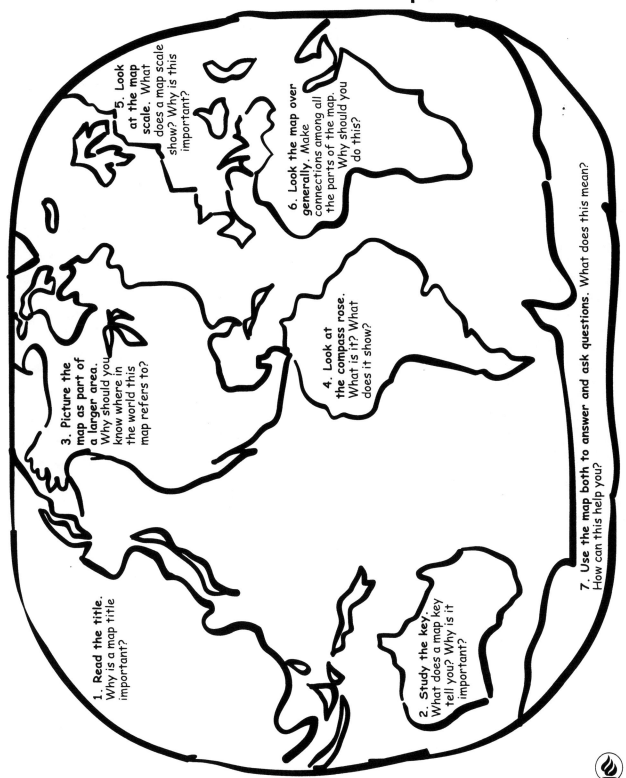

5. Look at the map scale. What does a map scale show? Why is this important?

6. Look the map over generally. Make connections among all the parts of the map. Why should you do this?

3. Picture the map as part of a larger area. Why should you know where in the world this map refers to?

4. Look at the compass rose. What is it? What does it show?

7. Use the map both to answer and ask questions. What does this mean? How can this help you?

1. Read the title. Why is a map title important?

2. Study the key. What does a map key tell you? Why is it important?

23

Name _____ Date _____

PPE-2: Locating a Place

Introduction: How would you describe the location of a place on earth? There are several ways to do it. The diagram shows how.

• **Directions:** Write the name of the place in the top box. Then provide the rest of the information.

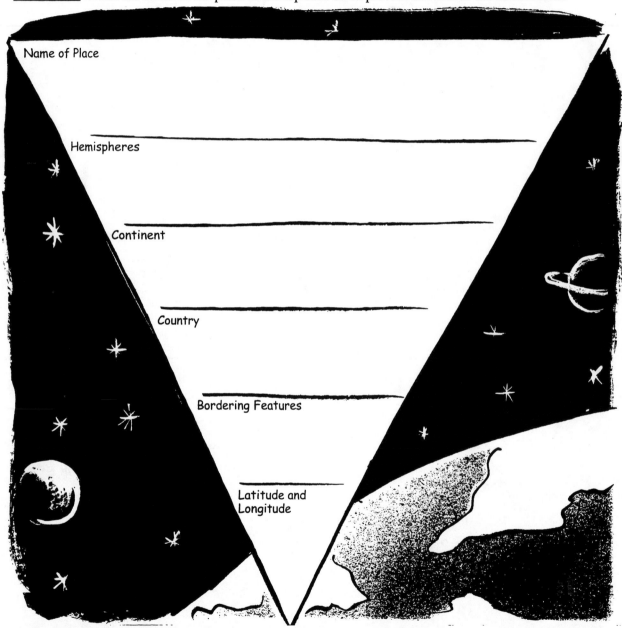

Name of Place

_____
Hemispheres

_____
Continent

_____
Country

_____
Bordering Features

_____
Latitude and
Longitude

Taking Another Step: In geography, there are two types of location. **Relative location** describes the location of a place in relation to other places. **Absolute location** describes the location of a place directly. On the back of this sheet, explain which of the items in the diagram refers to relative location and which refers to absolute location. Give reasons for your choices.

Name _____ Date _____

PPE-3: Characteristics of a Place or a Region

Introduction: Certain characteristics combine to make every place or region on earth unique. This diagram will help you identify these characteristics.

• **Directions:** Write the name of the place or region in the box provided. Then, complete each box on the right to identify its characteristics.

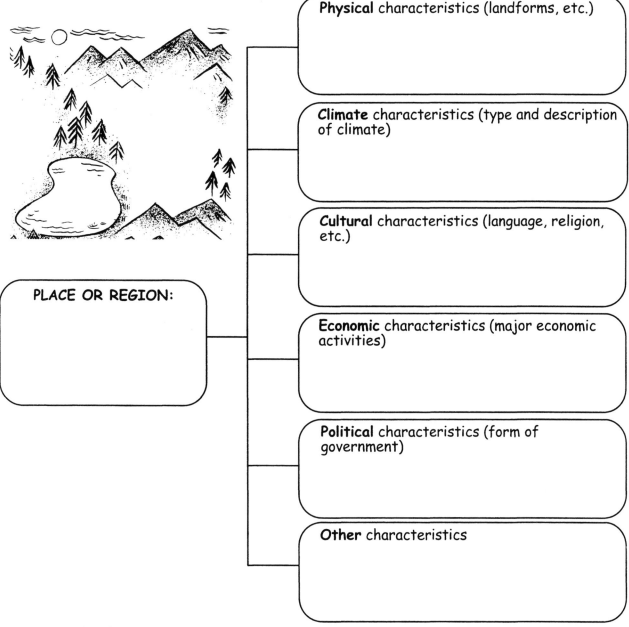

PLACE OR REGION:

Physical characteristics (landforms, etc.)

Climate characteristics (type and description of climate)

Cultural characteristics (language, religion, etc.)

Economic characteristics (major economic activities)

Political characteristics (form of government)

Other characteristics

Taking Another Step: On a separate sheet of paper, create a similar diagram for another place or region. Then, write a short essay in which you compare and contrast the two places or regions.

Name _____ Date _____

PPE-4: Profiling a Natural Feature

- **Directions:** Conduct research to complete the chart. Write short notes in each box.

Profile of _____
(name of natural feature)

Type of feature (mountain, river, desert, etc.)	
Location	
Measurements (altitude, length, area, etc.)	
How this feature was formed	
Nearby human settlements or activities	
How people use this feature or how it affects them	
Origin of name of feature	
Additional important information	

Taking Another Step: Sketch a map on the back of this sheet to show where in the world this natural feature is located.

Name _____ Date _____

PPE-5: The Three R's

<u>**Introduction:**</u> To combat pollution, everyone should follow "the three R's"—**Reduce, Reuse, Recycle**.

• <u>**Directions:**</u> Provide the information needed to complete the graphic organizer.

Fighting Pollution with "The Three R's"

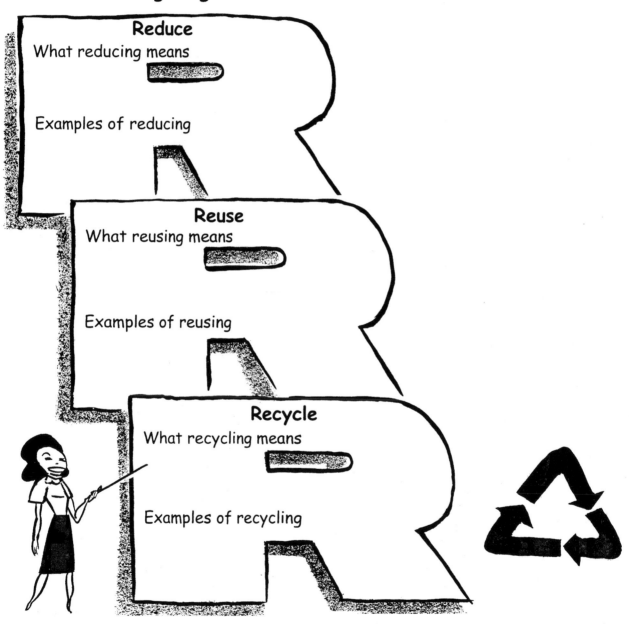

Reduce

What reducing means

Examples of reducing

Reuse

What reusing means

Examples of reusing

Recycle

What recycling means

Examples of recycling

<u>**Taking Another Step:**</u> On the back of this sheet, write a short essay that describes steps you can take to reduce, reuse, and recycle at home and at school.

Graphic Organizers for Social Studies Classes

IV. Individual Development and Identity (psychology)

IDI-1: Biographical Profile

Objective: Students will conduct research to create a biographical profile of a remarkable historical figure.

Key Questions:
- Questions formed from headings in the graphic organizer
- Why did you choose to do a profile of this person?

Usage Notes: Encourage students to fill out the profile completely. Consider assigning this graphic organizer in conjunction with reading biographies. Also, consider assigning this organizer in conjunction with graphic organizer IDI-2.

IDI-2: A Biographical Time Line

Objective: Students will conduct research to create a biographical time line of a remarkable historical figure.

Key Questions:
- What are the major events of this person's life?
- Why did you choose to learn more about this person?

Usage Notes: Make sure students understand the mechanics of the time line, as shown in the sample. Consider assigning this graphic organizer in conjunction with reading biographies. Also, consider assigning it in conjunction with graphic organizer IDI-1.

IDI-3: Personal Obstacles Overcome

Objective: Students will conduct research to identify the personal obstacles that a historical figure had to overcome, and apply what they learn to their own lives.

Key Questions:
- What obstacles did this person face?
- How did he or she overcome each one?
- What can you learn from this person's life and triumphs?

Usage Notes: Be careful to respect students' privacy when they complete the Taking Another Step activity.

IDI-4: Comparing and Contrasting Two Individuals

Objective: Students will compare and contrast two historical figures.

Key Questions:
- How are these two figures alike?
- How are they different?
- What can we learn from comparing and contrasting them?

Usage Notes: Make sure students understand the correct way to use a Venn diagram.

Name _____ Date _____

IDI-1: A Biographical Profile

Introduction: One of the best things about studying history is learning about fascinating people. In this activity, you will create a profile of the life of a remarkable historical figure.

• **Directions:** Write the name of the individual on the line provided. Then conduct research to complete the biographical profile.

A Biographical Profile of _____	
Nationality	
Life dates	
Major field (art, science, the military, etc.)	
Birthplace	
Family history	
Early life	
Education	
Major activities and contributions	
Additional interesting information	
Quotation	" "

Taking Another Step: On the back of this sheet, sketch a portrait of this individual, or create a symbol to represent his or her life.

Name _____ Date _____

IDI-2: A Biographical Time Line

Introduction: A **time line** is an excellent way to summarize the lives of historical figures. In this activity, you will create a time line of the life of a remarkable person.

• **Directions:** The tic marks, or lines, on the time line represent years. The space between each small tic represents one year. The space between the larger tics represents 10 years. Start your time line on the left. Label the first tic on the bottom with the nearest decade that began before the person's birth year. (For example, if the person was born in 1914, label the first tic 1910.) Then, label the other large tics in 10-year intervals (1920, 1930, etc.) Complete your time line by identifying important events on the left side of the time line and the year they took place along the right. The sample box will guide you.

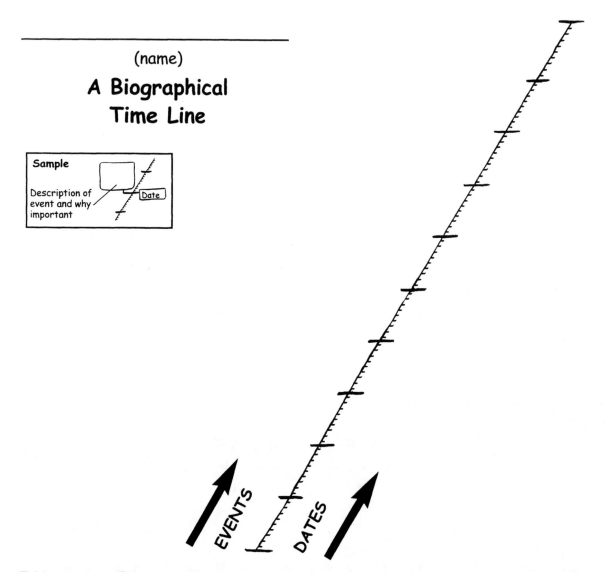

Taking Another Step: Create a similar time line of the major events in your own life. Use the back of this sheet.

Name _____ Date _____

IDI-3: Personal Obstacles Overcome

Introduction: Regardless of the problems or challenges you face, you can still achieve greatness. It might surprise you to learn that many famous people in history overcame tremendous personal hardships. For example, Franklin Delano Roosevelt became president despite being physically disabled.

• **Directions:** In this activity, you will consider the obstacles a historical figure had to overcome. Some examples might be personal health challenges, economic hardship, or opposition from other people. Write an obstacle in the spaces provided. Then, explain how this person overcame each one. Sketch in spaces for other obstacles if you need them.

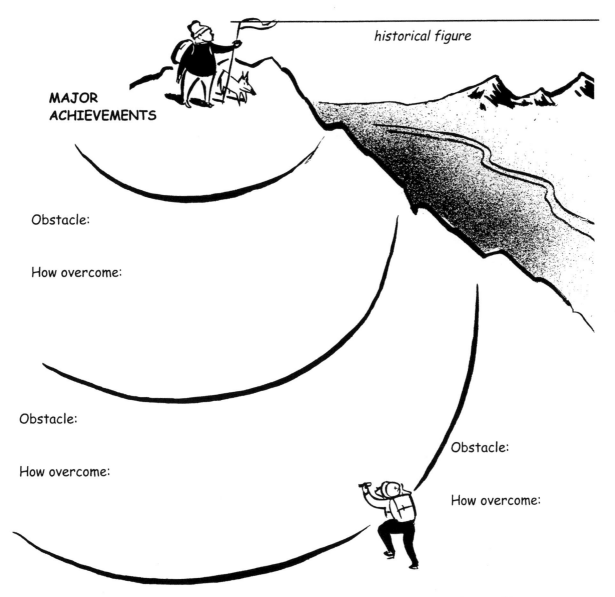

historical figure

MAJOR
ACHIEVEMENTS

Obstacle:

How overcome:

Obstacle:

How overcome:

Obstacle:

How overcome:

Taking Another Step: In a private journal article, write about the obstacles you face and how you can overcome them.

Name _____ Date _____

IDI-4: Comparing and Contrasting Two Individuals

Introduction: Comparing and contrasting two historical figures is a good way to learn more about both of them. Often, you'll be surprised to find out that two people are more alike, or more different, than you thought.

• **Directions:** Write the names of the individuals you are comparing and contrasting on the lines. Then, under their names, list characteristics that make each one unique. In the center area, list characteristics that they share(d). Characteristics you might consider include type of work, age, gender, when they lived, and so on.

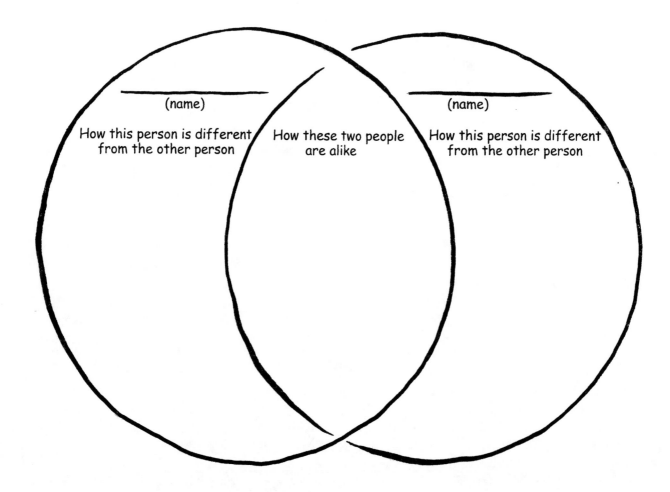

_____ (name)

How this person is different from the other person

How these two people are alike

_____ (name)

How this person is different from the other person

Taking Another Step: Draw a similar diagram on the back of this sheet. Use it to compare and contrast yourself with one of the people in this diagram or with another historical figure.

V. Individuals, Groups, and Institutions (sociology)

IGI-1: The American Population

Objective: Students will create a circle graph to show the racial and ethnic distribution of the population of the United States.

Key Questions:

- What percentage of the population does each group constitute?
- Which group constitutes the largest percentage? The smallest?
- Which two groups are nearly the same size?
- Why is it important to be aware of these percentages?

Usage Notes: Augment the activity by having students find the total population of the United States and convert each percentage into a population figure. Inform students that these percentages are approximate.

IGI-2: The Family

Objective: Students will discuss the family as the basic social unit in all societies and identify some important characteristics of the family.

Key Questions:

- Questions formed from headings in the graphic organizer
- What does "the family is the basic social unit in all societies" mean?

Usage Notes: Be careful to respect students' privacy when using this graphic organizer.

IGI-3: Major Steps in the Fight for Equal Rights

Objective: Students will identify major steps in the struggle for equal rights and describe each one's significance.

Key Questions:

- What steps did you include?
- When did each step occur?
- How was each step accomplished?
- What was the significance of each step?

Usage Notes: This graphic organizer was designed with the African-American civil rights movement in mind, but it can be used to depict other struggles for equality—such as equal rights for women in the U.S., and equality struggles in other eras and other countries.

IGI-4: Women in the United States Today

Objective: Students will investigate and report on the status of women in the United States today.

Key Questions:

- Questions formed from headings in the graphic organizer
- Why is it important to study women as a separate group?

Usage Notes: Use the "Other" boxes in the graphic organizer to tailor it to your particular needs.

Name _____ Date _____

IGI-1: The American Population

Introduction: The United States has the most diverse population of any country on earth. People from virtually every country have emigrated here. We have at least 120 distinct ethnic groups in the United States. Virtually every religion is practiced here, and hundreds of languages are spoken. This diversity is one of the most remarkable things about the American population.

• **Directions:** Use the information below to create a circle graph showing the diversity in the American population. Each tic (small line) on the graph represents 1 percent. The entire circle represents 100 percent.

The Population of the United States, Racial and Ethnic Composition	
Racial or Ethnic Group	**Percentage**
Total Population	100
Non-Hispanic White	75
African-American	12
Hispanic (Puerto Rican, Mexican, etc.)	10
Native American, Inuit, or Aleut	1
Asian or Pacific Islander	2

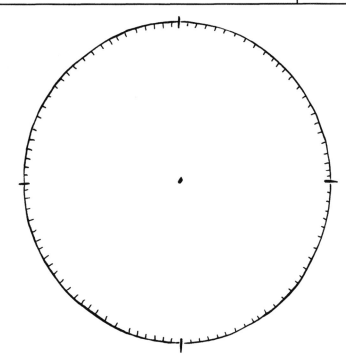

Taking Another Step: Does any of the information in the chart surprise you? Explain your answer. Use the back of this sheet.

Name _____ Date _____

IGI-2: The Family

Introduction: Families are the most important grouping of people in the world. This is because *the family is the basic social unit in every society.* The form the family takes varies from country to country and from culture to culture. Even within a country or a culture, the family can take many different forms. But, all families have important things in common.

• **Directions:** Think about how important families are as you complete the graphic organizer.

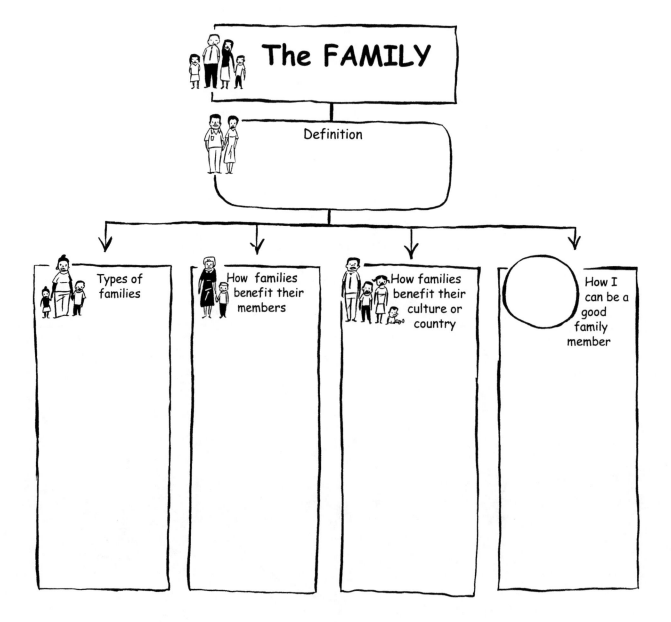

Taking Another Step: Draw a symbol that represents your family in the blank circle.

Name _____ Date _____ | **Student Activity Sheet** |

IGI-3. Major Steps in the Fight for Equal Rights

Introduction: One of the most significant stories in American history is the struggle for equal rights. That such a struggle was necessary to begin with is sad. But it is a great story because of the nobility of many people, the successes they achieved, and the example they set. In this activity, you will investigate some of the most important steps in this fight for freedom.

• **Directions:** Identify major steps in the struggle for equal rights. Also, identify when each step occurred and write a sentence that explains its significance.

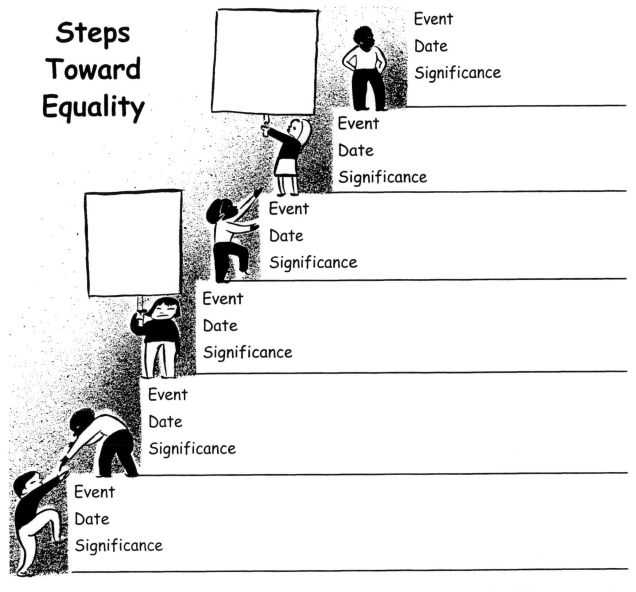

Steps Toward Equality

Event
Date
Significance

Event
Date
Significance

Event
Date
Significance

Event
Date
Significance

Event
Date
Significance

Event
Date
Significance

Taking Another Step: Add appropriate slogans to the signs that the figures are holding. Write a paragraph that identifies what you think the next step toward equality needs to be, and why.

39

Name _____ Date _____

IGI-4: Women in the United States Today

Introduction: As you know, women have not been treated equally to men throughout history. Although the twentieth century has seen significant progress toward equality, discrimination against women is still a fact of American life.

• **Directions:** Consult an almanac for the information you need to complete the chart.

Data Sheet: The American Woman	
Number of women in the United States	
Percentage of total U.S. population	
Percentage of women in the workforce	
Percentage of women who are married	
Percentage of women who are mothers	
Unique challenges faced by women	
Famous firsts	
Other _____ _____	
Other _____ _____	

Taking Another Step: Write a paragraph that identifies a woman you admire. Explain what qualities she has that you find admirable.

40

VI. Power, Authority, and Governance
(political science)

PAG-1: Representative Democracy in the United States

Objective: Students will explain the relationships among the people of the United States, the Constitution, the three branches of the federal government, and the three levels of government.

Key Questions:

- How does this diagram show that our government is based on the will of the people?

- Who has the authority to establish state governments? Local governments?

- How are members of the three branches of the federal government chosen?

Usage Notes: Walk students through the diagram, emphasizing the primacy of the people and the Constitution.

PAG-2: Amending the Constitution

Objective: Students will diagram and explain the process through which amendments are added to the Constitution.

Key Questions:

- What are the two methods of proposal?

- What are the two methods of ratification?

- How many different ways can the Constitution be amended?

Usage Notes: Encourage students to complete the Taking Another Step activity and use what they find to annotate their flow charts.

PAG-3: Checks and Balances in the Federal Government

Objective: Students will diagram and explain the system of checks and balances in the federal government.

Key Questions:

- What is the significance of each picture?

- What powers are unique to each branch of the federal government?

- How does each branch balance the power of the other two?

- How does each branch check the power of the other two?

- What does the phrase "checks and balances" mean?

Usage Notes: Guide students in making the connection between each branch and its representative building. Make sure students understand the mechanics of using the arrows: Each arrow points *toward* the branch that is being checked. Balance is represented by the powers listed in each box.

PAG-4: Federalism in the United States

Objective: Students will define *federalism* and explain how it is practiced in the United States.

Key Questions:

- What is federalism?

- Which powers of government are held only by the federal government? By the state governments? By both?

- Why do we have a federal system? What are its advantages and disadvantages?

Usage Notes: Ensure that students understand how to use a Venn diagram correctly.

PAG-5: A Local Government Profile

Objective: Students will create a profile of government in their community.

Key Questions:

- Questions formed from headings in the graphic organizer

- How did you locate this information?

Usage Notes: Guide students in conducting their research. Encourage them to contact and interview local government officials if possible.

Name _____ Date _____

PAG-1: Representative Democracy in the United States

Introduction: The United States is famous for government, as Abraham Lincoln put it, "of the people, by the people, for the people." Of course, the people of the United States don't make every governmental decision. We elect people to represent us. That's why we say we live in a **representative democracy**. But the people are the source of all laws and government at every level in the United States. To understand this relationship, complete the diagram.

• **Directions:** Complete the diagram by writing the terms from the box below in the correct locations.

charters	state constitutions	the judicial branch
Constitution	state governments	the legislative branch
local governments	the executive branch	

The People of the United States

created a document called the

Under this document, the people choose national leaders by electing members of two branches of the federal government.

The executive branch appoints

The Federal Government

By accepting _____

the federal government establishes ____

State governments grant _____

to establish

Taking Another Step: Why is it important that "The People of the United States" box is at the top of this diagram? Write your answer on the back of this sheet.

Name _____ Date _____

PAG-2: Amending the Constitution

Introduction: The Founders of the United States knew that the Constitution might need to change to reflect the changing needs of a growing nation. So, they included in the Constitution a process for **amending**, or adding to, the Constitution. This process can be shown in the form of a flow chart.

• **Directions:** Consult your textbook or other appropriate resources to complete the flow chart.

Constitutional Amendment

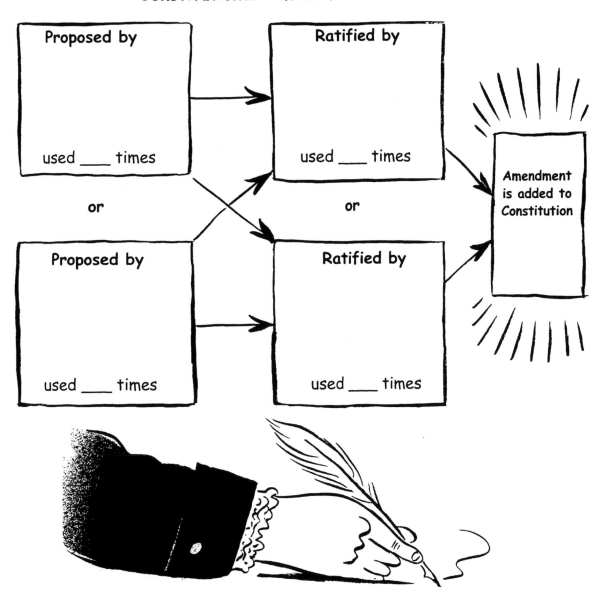

Taking Another Step: One method of proposal and one method of ratification have been used far more often than others. Identify these methods and explain why you think they have been used more frequently.

Name _____ Date _____

PAG-3: Checks and Balances in the Federal Government

Introduction: The writers of the U.S. Constitution were careful to design a government in which no one branch would become too powerful. To achieve this, they created a system of **checks and balances**, in which each branch can check, or limit, the actions of the other two. Each branch also has unique powers, to balance power among the three branches.

• **Directions:** Write the name of each branch of the federal government on the line in the correct box. Under its name, list that branch's major powers. Within the arrows, write the way each branch checks the power of the other two.

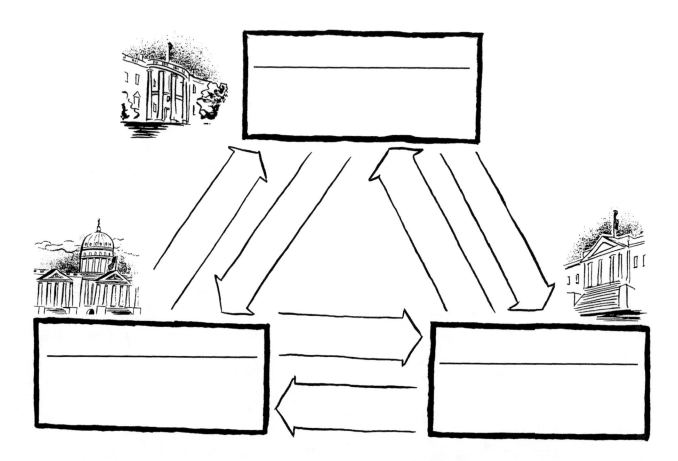

Taking Another Step: Write a paragraph that compares checks and balances in your state government with those in the federal government.

     Graphic Organizers for Social Studies Classes

Name _____ Date _____

PAG-4: Federalism in the United States

Introduction: The Constitution created a **federal system** of government in the United States. In a federal system, powers are shared between a national, or federal, government and state governments.

• **Directions:** List the major powers of the U.S. national government in the top circle. List the major powers of state governments in the bottom circle. List the powers that national and state governments share where the circles overlap.

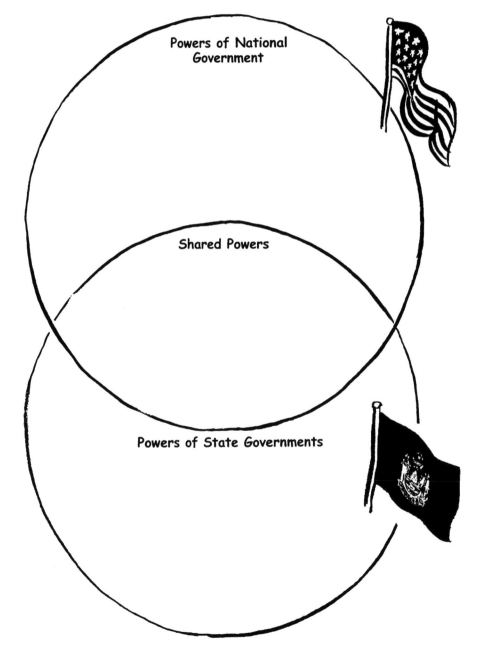

Powers of National Government

Shared Powers

Powers of State Governments

Taking Another Step: Sketch your own state flag on the back of this sheet.

Name _____ Date _____

PAG-5: A Local Government Profile

Introduction: How much do you know about government in your community? As a citizen of a democratic country you have the right—and the duty—to know about your local government and participate in it. The first step is to learn some basic facts about government in your community. Use this sheet as a guide.

• **Directions:** Complete the chart by conducting research. Visit the library to learn about local government. Also, use the telephone book to call community officials and ask them questions.

My Community Government	
Type of government (town, commission, council-manager, etc.)	
Names and titles of major community officials (mayor, manager, commissioners, etc.)	
Major services provided by community government	

Taking Another Step: On the back of this sheet, write a paragraph that identifies at least two ways that you could participate in your local government.

VII. Production, Distribution, and Consumption (economics)

PDC-1: The Factors of Production

Objective: Students will identify the four factors of production (land, capital, labor, management), describe each, and give examples of each.

Key Questions:

- What are the four factors of production? Describe each one.

- What are some examples of each factor of production?

- How is each factor necessary for production of goods and services?

Usage Notes: Extend the activity by challenging students to explain how all four factors of production apply in a local business.

PDC-2: The Business Cycle

Objective: Students will describe and diagram the business cycle.

Key Questions:

- What is the business cycle?

- What are the parts of the business cycle? What characterizes each part?

- Why is understanding the business cycle important?

Usage Notes: Introduce the terms *recession* and *depression* and have students explain them in the context of the business cycle.

PDC-3: Becoming a Wise Consumer

Objective: Students will list several techniques they can use to become smart consumers.

Key Questions:

- What tips are on your list?

- How can each one help you?

Usage Notes: Have students compare their lists and create a master list as a class.

Name _____ Date _____

PDC-1: The Factors of Production

Introduction: To produce any good or provide any service, it takes many things. Of course, those things vary from business to business. But, whatever the business, everything it needs to produce a good or provide a service falls into one of four major categories. Together, these four categories are known as the **factors of production**.

• **Directions:** Complete the diagram: Label the four factors of production, define each, and give examples.

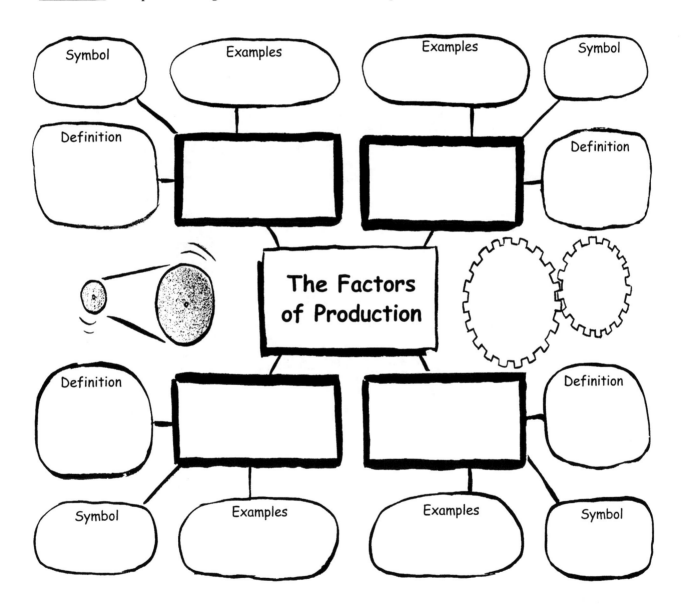

Taking Another Step: Next to each "Symbol" circle, draw a symbol to represent a factor of production.

51

Name _____ Date _____

PDC-2: The Business Cycle

Introduction: As you may be aware, the American economy has ups and downs—better times and worse times. This tendency of the economy to swing from good to bad and back again, over and over, is called the **business cycle.**

• **Directions**: Use the information in the box to label the diagram correctly. Use the boldface words only. You will use each term more than once.

Stages of the Business Cycle

Expansion: Period of the business cycle during which the total amount of goods and services produced by the economy is increasing

Peak: High point of the business cycle; follows an expansion and precedes a contraction

Contraction: Period of the business cycle during which the total amount of goods and services produced by the economy is decreasing

Trough: Low point on a business cycle; follows a contraction and precedes an expansion

---

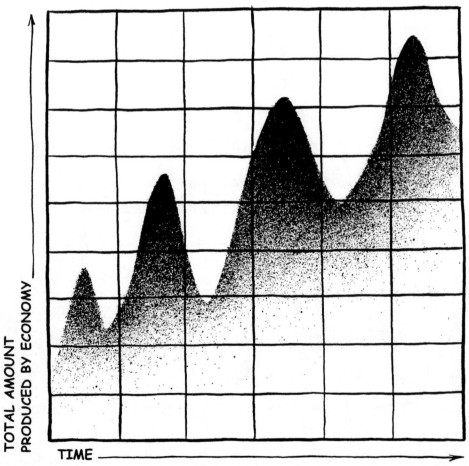

Taking Another Step: Why is it very important for consumers, business people, and government officials to know where in the business cycle we are?

                     Graphic Organizers for Social Studies Classes

Name _____ Date _____

PDC-3: Becoming a Wise Consumer

Introduction: Before you go shopping, you should make a list, but not just of things to buy. You should also make a list of ways to shop carefully! There's a Latin phrase, *caveat emptor,* that means "let the buyer beware," or "buy at your own risk." You'll do well to remember it. Despite the many laws that exist to protect consumers, it's still your responsibility to shop wisely.

• **Directions:** List as many smart shopping tips as you can. Explain how each will help you.

Taking Another Step: Check off the tips you have actually used.

VIII.   Science, Technology, and Society (multidisciplinary)

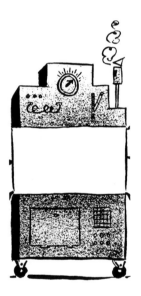

STS-1: Understanding Science and Technology

Objective: Students will define and compare and contrast science and technology.

Key Questions:
- What is science? technology?
- How are they similar? different?
- What are some examples of science? technology?
- Why is it especially important to understand science and technology in the modern age?

Usage Notes: Emphasize the important differences between the two terms, which in informal usage are often treated like interchangeable synonyms.

STS-2: Profiling a Technology

Objective: Students will conduct research to create a profile of a technology.

Key Questions:
- Questions formed from headings in the graphic organizer

Usage Notes: Emphasize the central role that technology plays in modern life, and how it can benefit students to have a good understanding of the technology that affects their lives so profoundly.

STS-3: An Invention—Causes and Effects

Objective: Students will identify and explain the precursors to an invention and identify and explore the invention's effects.

Key Questions:
- What were the sources, or causes, of this invention?
- What effects did this invention have?
- Were the effects positive, negative, or both? Explain.

Usage Notes: Ensure that students understand what is meant by "causes" in this flow chart. Work to ensure that students view individual inventions in a larger historical context.

STS-4: Performing a Cost-Benefit Analysis

Objective: Students will identify the costs and benefits of a technology and weigh them against each other.

Key Questions:
- What are the advantages, or benefits, of this technology?
- What are the disadvantages, or costs, of this technology?
- Do the benefits outweigh the costs? Explain.

Usage Notes: Explain how every technology, no matter how beneficial, entails some costs.

Name _____ Date _____

STS-1: Understanding Science and Technology

Introduction: You hear the words *science* and *technology* all the time, often used together. But do you know whether these terms mean the same thing? Or do they refer to very different things? You need to know. Science and technology are so important today that our age is called both the scientific age and the technological age. Science and technology affect your life in dramatic ways every day. So knowing and using the words **science** and **technology** properly is crucial for making sense of the world.

• **Directions:** Use your notes, textbook, and other appropriate resources to complete the graphic organizer.

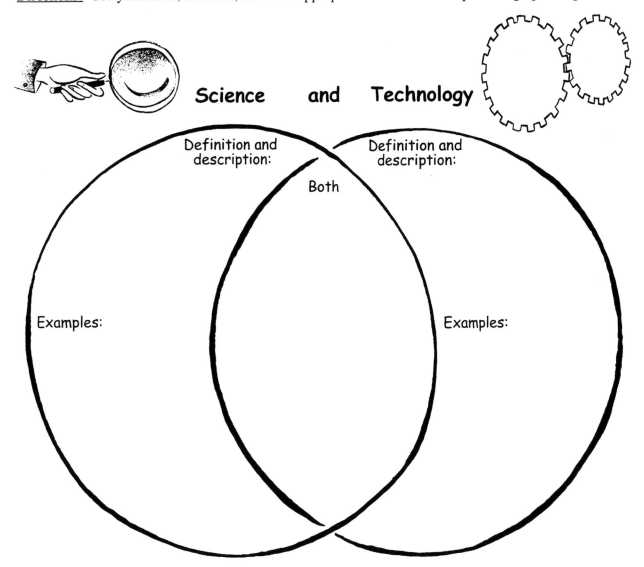

Taking Another Step: Some people refer to technology as "science in action" or "science put to use." What do they mean? Write your answer on the back of this sheet.

Name _____ Date _____

STS-2: Profiling a Technology

Introduction: There are thousands of technologies being used around the world at this very moment. From ballpoint pens to jet airplanes, from computers to waterwheels, ours is a world of technology. In this activity, you will identify the key facts about one technology.

• **Directions:** Write the name of the technology you are investigating on the line. Then conduct research to complete as much of the chart as possible.

_____ : KEY FACTS *(name of technology)*	
Purpose or use	
When invented or developed	
Where invented or developed	
Principal people involved in invention or development	
Energy source	
People who use it	
Where used	
Additional information	

Taking Another Step: Why is it important for you to know the type of information included in the chart about *many different types* of technology? Write your answer on the back of this sheet.

Name _____ Date _____

STS-3: An Invention—Causes and Effects

Introduction: Inventions don't come out of the blue. Every inventor has relied, in one way or another, on existing knowledge and technology. For example, the Wright brothers used knowledge of kites, of other gliders, and even of bicycle mechanics when they invented the airplane. No single development led to the airplane, but when the Wright brothers combined existing knowledge and added to it, they were able to invent something revolutionary. Similarly, an invention doesn't have just a single effect. The Wright brothers couldn't imagine today's huge jet airliners and what they mean for international travel and relations. This activity examines an invention's multiple sources and its multiple effects.

• **Directions:** Identify a real invention in the center box. In the left-hand column, identify what led to the invention (for example, certain information or pressing needs, existing technology, other inventions). In the right-hand column, identify as many effects as possible that the invention has had.

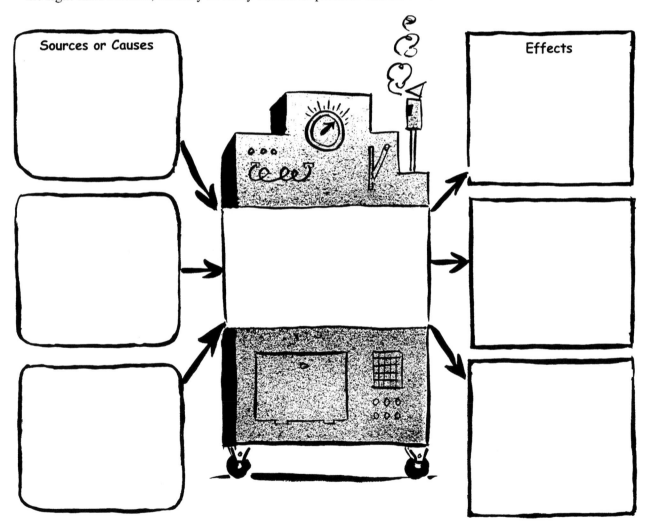

Taking Another Step: Given what you listed in the left-hand column, do you think this invention was inevitable? In other words, if the inventor hadn't thought it up, was somebody else bound to? Explain. Write your answer on the back of this sheet.

Name _____ Date _____ | **Student Activity Sheet** |

STS-4: Performing a Cost-Benefit Analysis

Introduction: Think about a motor vehicle—a car or a truck. What are the benefits of this technology? Ease of transportation, speed, convenience . . . there are very many. Now think about the *dis*advantages. Air pollution, traffic jams, sprawling cities . . . there are very many. The point is that every technology has advantages and disadvantages. Advantages are sometimes called **benefits**; disadvantages are sometimes called **costs**. In our world, where technology plays such a huge role in everyday life, understanding the costs and benefits of technologies is critical.

• **Directions:** Use your notes, your textbook, and any other appropriate resources to complete the chart. First, choose a technology. Then investigate and record its costs and benefits.

Costs and Benefits of a Technology	
Technology: _____	
Costs (–)	**Benefits (+)**

Taking Another Step: A cost-benefit analysis is a study that weighs the costs of a technology against its benefits to see if the technology is worthwhile. Do you think the benefits of this technology outweigh its costs? Explain your reasoning. Write your answer on the back of this sheet.

IX.   Global Connections (multidisciplinary)

GC-1: The Global Economy

Objective: Students will investigate the manufacture and raw materials of a common object to see it as an example of the global economy.

Key Questions:
- Where was the object manufactured?
- Where did the raw materials come from?
- How did worldwide communication and transportation networks figure into creating this object and moving it here?

Usage Notes: Students should start their research by searching for a "Made in" stamp.

GC-2: The Internet

Objective: Students will answer key questions about the Internet and the World Wide Web.

Key Questions:
- Questions from the graphic organizer

Usage Notes: Emphasize how influential the Internet will be throughout students' lives. Compare it to television in the middle decades of the twentieth century.

GC-3: International Communications:

Objective: Students will list methods of international communications and key facts about them.

Key Questions:
- Questions formed from headings in graphic organizer
- What do all of these methods of communication have in common?
- How does modern life depend on these communication methods?

Usage Notes: Students can work in small groups to brainstorm items for the first column.

GC-4: The United Nations:

Objective: Students will research and explain the organization of the United Nations.

Key Questions:
- How is the United Nations organized?
- What is the primary function of each organ?
- What are the specialized agencies?

Usage Notes: Link the particular organs and agencies in the diagram with current news events about their activities.

Name _____ Date _____

GC-1: The Global Economy

Introduction: Look at a pencil—you may even have one in your hand right now. This humble object is perhaps the best symbol of the global connections that exist in the world today. First, because pencils— billions upon billions of them—are found throughout the world. And second, because the raw materials that went into making the pencil came from nearly everywhere on earth. The pencil itself was probably manufactured in North America. The materials to manufacture it came from all over the world: copper from South America, crude oil from Europe, castor oil from Africa, graphite from Asia, and zinc from Australia. All of these materials came together through a global network of transportation (ships, aircraft, railways, and trucks) and communication (telephones, faxes, satellites, and computers). When you hold a pencil in your hand, you are also holding the world.

• **Directions:** This activity traces the global origins of a common classroom object. First, choose an object. Then, conduct research to determine how it was made. Find out where the raw materials to make it came from. Put your information in the diagram. In each box, list a point of manufacture or a raw material at its point of origin. Add boxes and arrows to the diagram as needed.

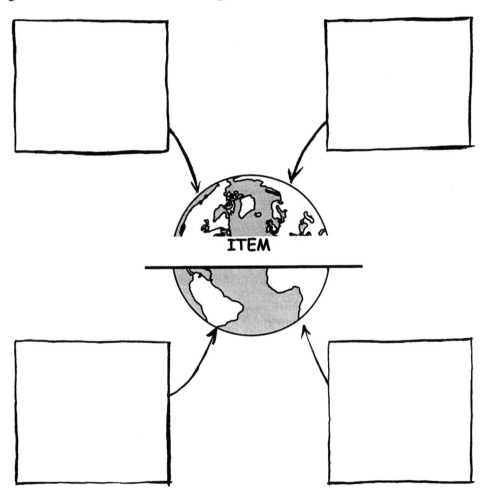

Taking Another Step: Write a paragraph on the back of this sheet that explains how the object you investigated is a symbol of the global economic, transportation, and communication networks.

Name _____ Date _____

GC-2: The Internet

Introduction: You've probably at least heard of the Internet and the World Wide Web, but can you describe them? Do you know how to use them to help you in and out of school? You need to. These global computer networks are changing the way we work, play, solve problems, and even think about our world. In this activity, you answer several questions that will help you understand this revolution in the way people live.

• **Directions:** Conduct research to answer each question.

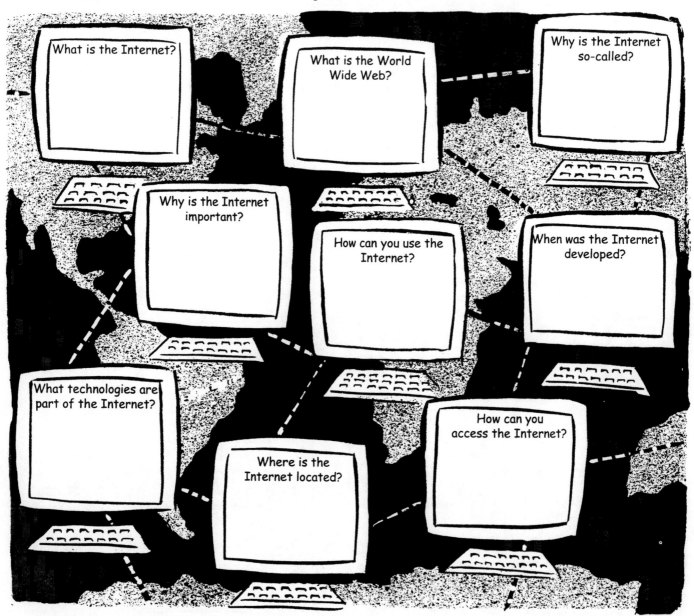

What is the Internet?

What is the World Wide Web?

Why is the Internet so-called?

Why is the Internet important?

How can you use the Internet?

When was the Internet developed?

What technologies are part of the Internet?

Where is the Internet located?

How can you access the Internet?

Taking Another Step: If you've used the Internet, describe your most rewarding experience on it. If you haven't used it, write an action plan that will enable you to try it out. Use the back of this sheet.

Name _____ Date _____

GC-3: International Communications

Introduction: How many ways to communicate can you think of? Your answer will certainly be much longer than the one your parents would have given when they were in school. The past few decades have seen remarkable changes in how people communicate. All of these developments are electronic (for example, fax machines, e-mail, satellite communications, and cellular telephones). In this activity you will develop a firm understanding of the communication technologies that are available to you. The focus is on methods of communication that are international—those that allow us to communicate with people in other countries.

• **Directions:** Conduct research to complete the chart.

Modern Methods of International Communication				
Method of Communication	**Description**	**Primary Uses**	**When invented or developed**	**Advantages and disadvantages**

Taking Another Step: Put an asterisk (*) next to the methods of communication you have used. Then, choose one you have not yet used and explain why you would like a chance to use it. Write your explanation on the back of this sheet.

Name _____ Date _____

GC-4: The Organization of the United Nations

Introduction: The premier international organization is the **United Nations**. Most countries in the world are members of the UN, and the UN has played a key role in international conflicts and cooperation for more than half a century.

• **Directions:** The diagram shows how the United Nations is organized. Use an encyclopedia or another appropriate resource to complete the diagram. Write the name of each major part, or organ, of the UN in the ovals. Include a brief description of each part's purpose. In the Specialized Agencies box, list the UN's specialized agencies.

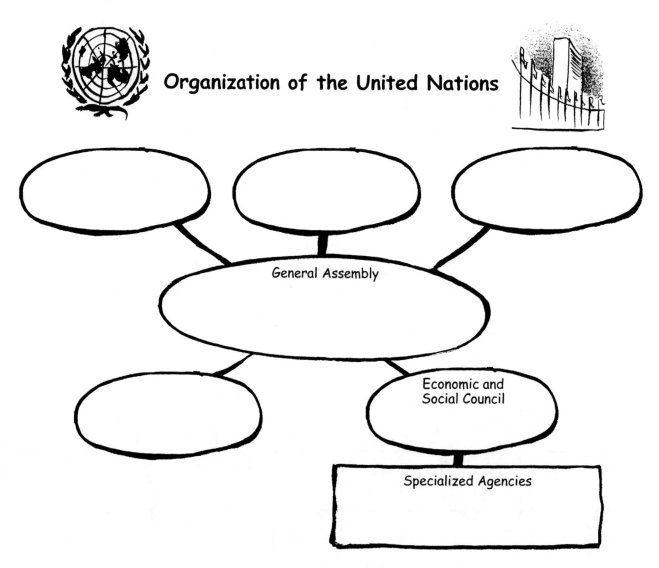

Organization of the United Nations

General Assembly

Economic and Social Council

Specialized Agencies

Taking Another Step: Study the United Nations symbol. Why do you think the map is centered on the North Pole, and not on a continent? Why do you think the map is surrounded by olive branches?

X.   Civic Ideals and Practices
(multidisciplinary)

CIP-1: Understanding Citizenship

Objective: Students will define and describe citizenship and identify ways to be better citizens.

Key Questions:

- Questions formed from headings in graphic organizer

Usage Notes: Encourage students to see how they personally benefit from the good citizenship of others.

CIP-2: Duties and Responsibilities of Citizenship

Objective: Students will identify and explain the duties and responsibilities of citizenship.

Key Questions:

- How is "duties of citizenship" defined?

- What are the duties of citizenship?

- How is "responsibilities of citizenship" defined?

- What are the responsibilities of citizenship?

- How are duties and responsibilities alike? Different?

Usage Notes: Duties include obeying the law, paying taxes, appearing in court, etc. Responsibilities include voting, being respectful to others, helping others, etc.

CIP-3: Rights of Citizenship

Objective: Students will identify the rights of American citizens and explain how they are guaranteed by the Constitution.

Key Questions:

- What rights do American citizens have?

- What are some ways in which we exercise each?

- How is each one protected?

Usage Notes: Endeavor to develop in students an appreciation and respect of these rights.

Name _____ Date _____

CIP-1: Understanding Citizenship

Introduction: The word *citizen* simply means a member of a nation. **Citizenship** refers to being a good citizen. But what does good citizenship mean in your daily life? How can you be a better citizen? Why is it important to be a good citizen? This activity answers these and other questions about citizenship.

• **Directions:** Write your answers below.

Citizenship

What citizenship is

Why being a good citizen is important

Qualities of a good citizen

What can I do to be a better citizen

At home

At school

In my community

Taking Another Step: Take one of the steps you listed under "What I can do to be a better citizen." Write a journal entry that describes how and why you did it, and how it made you feel.

Name _____ Date _____

CIP-2: Duties and Responsibilities of Citizenship

Introduction: Being a citizen of the United States gives you important rights. But, in some ways, even more important are the *duties* and *responsibilities* of citizenship. The **duties** of citizenship include the things that the law requires of you as a citizen. For example, you are required to obey the law. The **responsibilities** of citizenship are not required by law, but good citizens fulfill them anyway. For example, responsible citizens vote in elections and participate in government, although law does not require it. When you carry out both the duties and responsibilities of citizenship, you are being the best citizen you can be.

• **Directions:** How many duties and responsibilities of citizenship can you think of? List them all below.

My Duties as a Citizen

My Responsibilities as a Citizen

Taking Another Step: On the back of this sheet, write a paragraph in which you honestly evaluate how well you perform the responsibilities of citizenship.

Name _____ Date _____

CIP-3: Rights of Citizenship

Introduction: American citizens have more rights than the people of any other country. Unfortunately, many of us take these rights for granted, forgetting that millions of people in the world live without them. Millions have also fought and died, and continue to do so, for a chance to have the same rights we enjoy every day. Very many Americans struggled in many ways to earn and protect these rights. So, it is truly important that you know and appreciate your rights as an American citizen.

• **Directions:** In the left-hand column, list as many rights as you can that American citizens enjoy. If your teacher so directs, complete the right-hand column by identifying the part of the Constitution that guarantees each right.

The Rights of American Citizens	
Right	Part of Constitution that Guarantees Right

Taking Another Step: On the back of this sheet, write a paragraph that tells which of the rights listed you exercised in the past week. Explain how you exercised each right.

Additional Graphic Tools
(multidisciplinary)

The graphic organizers in this section are self-explanatory. They are also very flexible, so you can assign them in a variety of classroom situations, as you see fit.

Name _____ Date _____

AGT-1: United States Outline Map

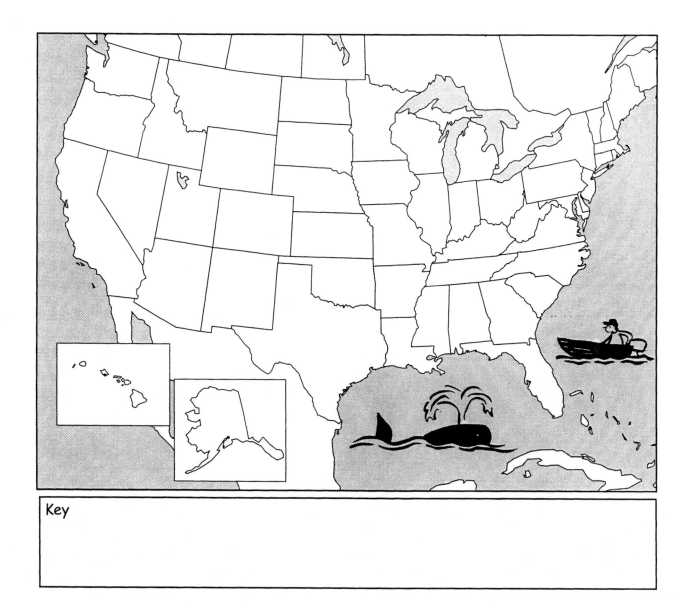

Key

Name _____ Date _____

AGT-2: World Outline Map

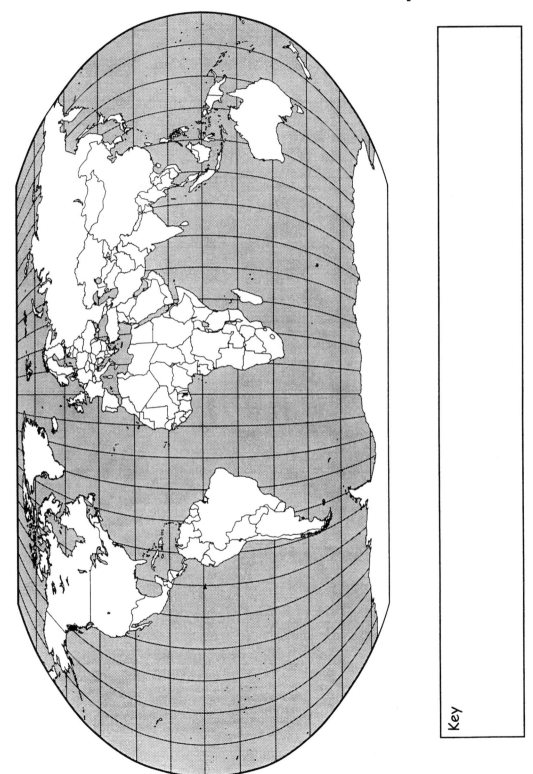

Key

75 *Graphic Organizers for Social Studies Classes*

Name _____ Date _____

AGT-3: Bar Graph Template

Name _____ Date _____

AGT-4: Line Graph Template

Name _____ Date _____

AGT-5: Circle Graph Template

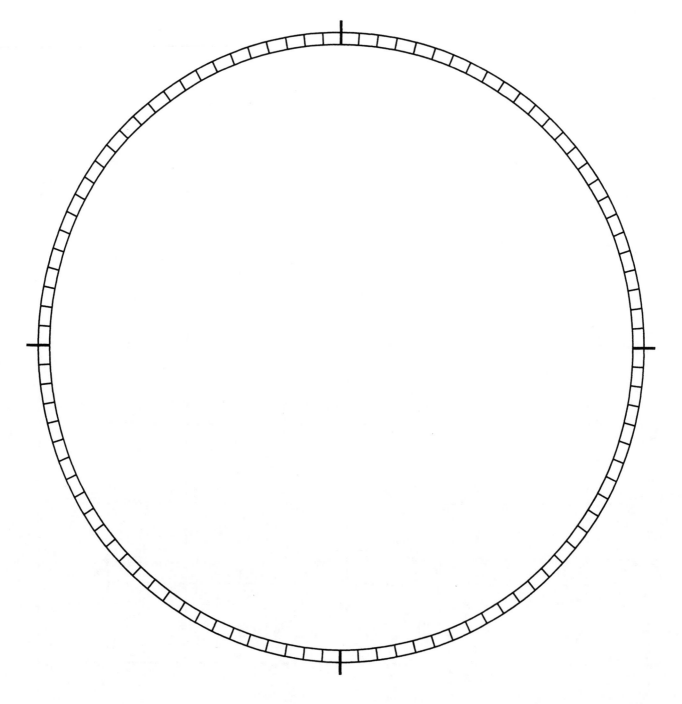

Name _____ Date _____

AGT-6: Venn Diagram Template

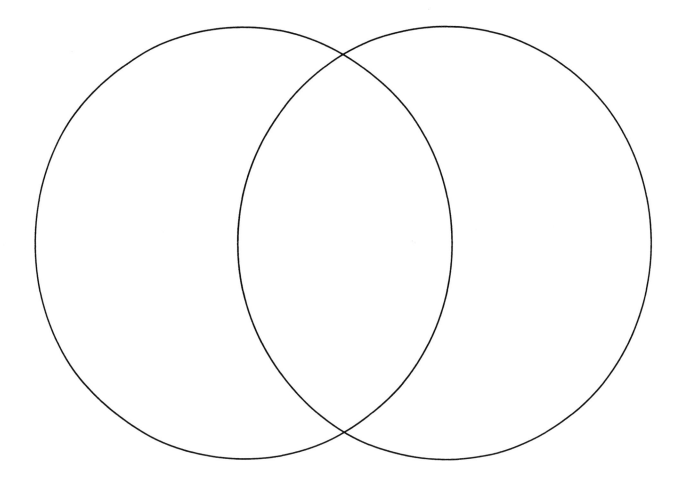

Graphic Organizers for Social Studies Classes

Name _____ Date _____

AGT-7: Time Line Template

_____

(Title)

Dates   Dates

|++|

Events   Events

Name _____ Date _____

AGT-8: A K-W-L Chart

Introduction: K-W-L stands for What I *K*now, What I *W*ant to Know, and What I *L*earned. Filling out a K-W-L chart before, during, and after a project is a good way to keep track of your progress.

• **Directions:** Complete the K-W-L chart.

Activity or Assignment: _____

K (complete before)	W (complete before)	L (complete during and after)
What do you already know about the subject?	What do you want to learn about the subject?	What did you learn about the subject?

Name _____ Date _____

AGT-9: The Six Questions:

Who?

Where?

Subject:

What?

Why?

How?

How?

Name _____ Date _____

AGT-10: Main Idea and Details

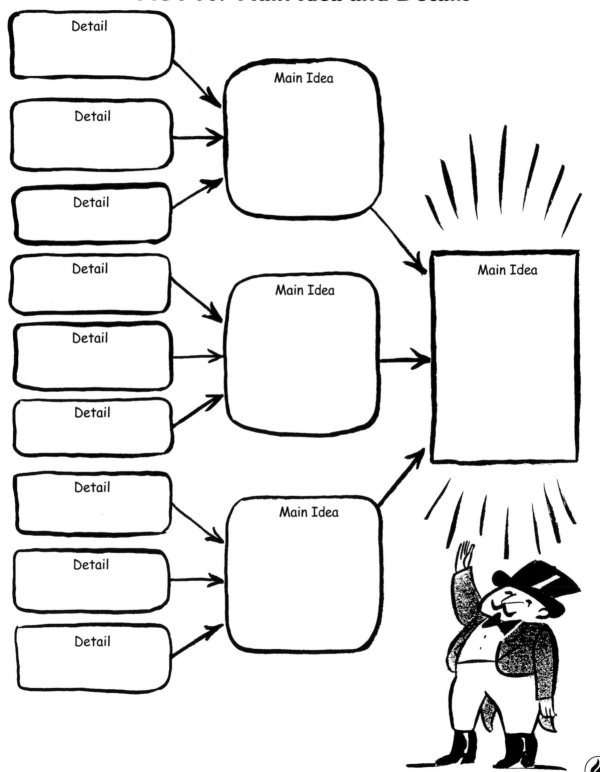

Name _____ Date _____

AGT-11: Personal Glossary

Introduction: A **glossary** is a list of specialized terms and their meanings. As you progress through the school year, you will learn many new terms. This sheet gives you a place to create a personal glossary of these terms.

• **Directions:** As you learn new terms, record them and their meanings in the chart below.

Terms Related to My Study of _____	
Term	**Definition**

       Graphic Organizers for Social Studies Classes